REFRIGERATOR ART

REFRIGERATOR ART

by Gary Wise and Lance Aldrich

Another Real Life Adventures Collection

Andrews and McMeel
A Universal Press Syndicate Company
Kansas City

ATTENTION: SCHOOLS AND BUSINESSES

Andrews and McMeel books are available at quantity discounts with bulk purchase for educational, business, or sales promotional use. For information, write to: Special Sales Department, Andrews and McMeel, 4520 Main Street, Kansas City, Missouri 64111.

Real Life Adventures

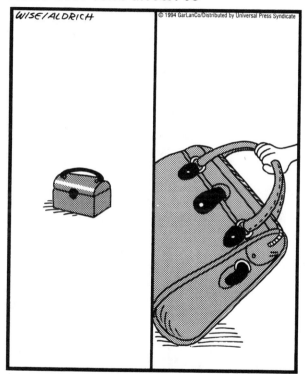

Purses come in two sizes: too small to get anything into, and too big to lift.

Real Life Adventures

... THE PLAYER TO THE RIGHT THEN MUST HAVE 6 BEEBLES (2 OF WHICH MUST BE WOMBLES) TO ADVANCE TO THE WHOOPEE LEVEL. IF NO ONE HAS BEEBLES, THE PLAYER WITH THE MOST GEEZLGAKS MAY BID FOR THE HAPPY STICK.

GarLanCo

Beebles™

FUN FOR ALL AGES!

Board games: It isn't whether you win or lose; it's whether you can figure out the rules.

Real Life Adventures

Driver has kids in college.

Real Life Adventures

A self-fulfilling prophecy.

Real Life Adventures

Real Life Pie Chart.

Real Life Adventures

While it may be a source of pride for you, the ability to pick things up with your toes is generally unappreciated by the general public.

Real Life Adventures

Why not move that exercise bike into the kitchen where you can put it to good use?

Real Life Adventures

Suggestion box.   **Suggestion barrel.**

Real Life Adventures

Forgetting to enter a check is
your ticket to adventure.

Real Life Adventures

When men "slip into something more
comfortable," it's anything but romantic.

Real Life Adventures

Another reason you can't go home again:
People there know the nickname
you had when you were a kid.

Real Life Adventures

Things that need doing around the house
are invisible to men.

Real Life Adventures

Nobody really wants to know how you are.

Real Life Adventures

"The Real Life Gardener Show."

Real Life Adventures

When autumn leaves fall, they have just enough strength left to lift your windshield wipers and crawl under them.

Real Life Adventures

"Saving things for the kids" is short for "saving old outdated things for the kids that they won't want and will toss out at the very first Dumpster they come to."

Real Life Adventures

Revenge tip: Why not make it as painful
for the dentist as it is for you?

Real Life Adventures

How stop signs apparently read to most people.

Real Life Adventures

To you, it's a foot. To your cat, it's a target.

Real Life Adventures

ACCORDING TO THESE PAPERS I FOUND IN TIMMY'S ROOM, HE OWNS SEVERAL OFFICE BUILDINGS DOWNTOWN.

What kids do with all the change
they never give back.

Real Life Adventures

Actually, the founding mothers were really the people behind things.

Real Life Adventures

To get eaten at the office, it doesn't have to be good. It just has to be free.

It's true: Men *are* after only one thing.

You can tell when parents of young children aren't getting out enough.

Real Life Adventures

Department of Corrections.

Real Life Adventures

To make the dining experience more interesting, many restaurants have special evenings.

Real Life Adventures

Where the Boulevard of Broken Dreams crosses the Boulevard of Broken Axles.

Real Life Adventures

Finishing a jigsaw puzzle is easy once you figure out the secret.

Real Life Adventures

The unwelcome mat.

Real Life Adventures

**Carrying massive, enormous heavy things alone:
It's a guy thing.**

Real Life Adventures

Repressed memories.

Real Life Adventures

According to the predictions made back in the '50s, you're supposed to be living in a space station and commuting in a rocket suit by now.

Before going visiting, be sure to brush up on the "time to go home" signs.

Taking messages is not a skill kids are born with.

The perfect marriage.

How to make your own airline pillow.

Finding a great parking spot in the winter isn't luck; it's an incredibly deep slush puddle that everybody else had the sense to avoid.

Pregnancy causes morning sickness long after the baby is born.

Real Life Adventures

Bridge: the perfect game for those who don't find quantum physics challenging enough.

Real Life Adventures

Kids know instinctively which parent is the soft touch for any given situation.

Real Life Adventures

If you're having trouble sleeping, go to a meeting.

Real Life Adventures

The view from the Gawker Copter.

Real Life Adventures

Manliness is simply an advanced form of boyliness.

Real Life Adventures

The power of positive thinking is no match for the power of negative doing.

Real Life Adventures

Gullible's Travels.

Real Life Adventures

Answering somebody else's phone is a dangerous thing to do.

Real Life Adventures

The autopsy will determine that the cause of death was an ill-advised comment regarding the pot roast.

Real Life Adventures

Millions of years from now, paleontologists will discover fossilized underwear under what was, at one time, the husband's side of the bed.

Real Life Adventures

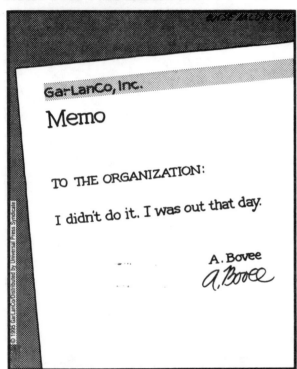

The appropriate length of any memo is just long enough to entirely cover your butt.

Real Life Adventures

Maybe having your swing analyzed by a golf pro isn't such a good idea.

Real Life Adventures

The sound barrier: what surrounds most husbands.

Real Life Adventures

Family get-togethers let families remember why they don't get together more often.

Real Life Adventures

Do you have to say "hi" every time?
Or does one "hi" cover you for the day?

Real Life Adventures

People with neat, clean garages
leave them open just to taunt you.

Real Life Adventures

When men and women get engaged,
shouldn't the guy get a ring, too?

Real Life Adventures

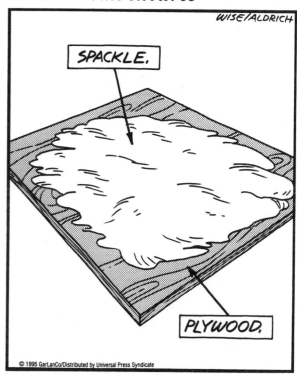

Save money. Make your own toaster pastries.

Real Life Adventures

It's not a good sign when your
mechanic knows your voice.

Real Life Adventures

White-collar blues.

Real Life Adventures

The scariest sounds are the ones you hear in the middle of the night.

Real Life Adventures

What used to be called "kissing up" and "using your friends" is now called "networking."

Another car owner adding washer fluid
to the valve cover, the intake manifold,
the spark plugs, and the driveway.

Parent-teacher conferences: when parents
go to school to learn more about their kids
than they ever wanted to know.

Real Life Adventures

The sign of a person who has unloaded the
dishwasher one too many times.

Real Life Adventures

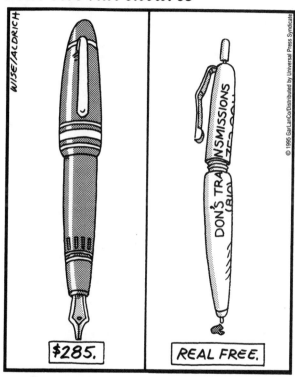

Pens you lose.   Pens you never lose.

Real Life Adventures

Real Life Adventures

Moving furniture is easy compared with
moving the cat off the furniture.

Real Life Adventures

Either real good, or real bad.

Real Life Adventures

Gawkers at a horrible crash on the information superhighway.

Real Life Adventures

The perfect watch for work.

Real Life Adventures

Blame is like butter: It's better
for you if you spread it thin.

Real Life Adventures

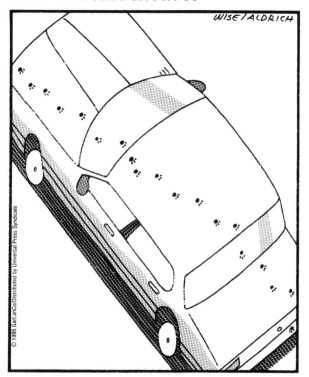

To a cat, the shortest distance
between two points is across your car.

Real Life Adventures

In the sleeping-position battle, it's not a fight for
the upper hand. It's a fight for the upper leg.

Real Life Adventures

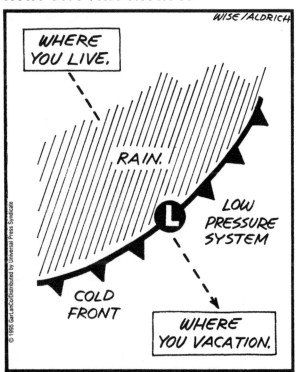

How weather fronts move.

Real Life Adventures

What most companies need is
a disorganization chart.

Real Life Adventures

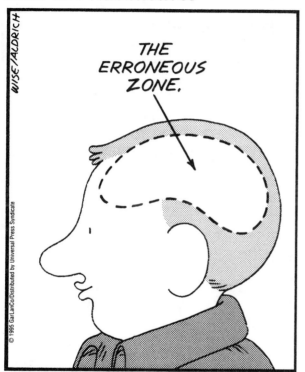

Real Life Adventures

Airline fact: Coach seats are spaced just far enough apart so the kid behind you can reach yours with his feet.

Real Life Adventures

WISE/ALDRICH   © 1995 GarLanCo/Distributed by Universal Press Syndicate

GO SEE IF HE'S IN THERE.

YOU GO SEE IF HE'S IN THERE.

·MEN·

Your worst work nightmare: something so awful, so urgent, they come looking for you in the bathroom.

Real Life Adventures

MY CLIENT WOULD LIKE TO WATCH ESPN FROM 2 TO 4 PM ON SATURDAYS, AFTER WHICH HE WILL BE HAPPY TO DO YARD WORK. HE IS ALSO WILLING TO TRADE TWO HOURS OF WALLPAPERING FOR ONE PLAY-OFF SERIES, SPORT TO BE NAMED LATER.

© 1995 GarLanCo/Distributed by Universal Press Syndicate   WISE/ALDRICH

Perhaps you need a sports agent to negotiate for you.

Real Life Adventures

The term "confidential fax" is an oxymoron.

Real Life Adventures

Rules were made to be made.

It's good to have career goals.

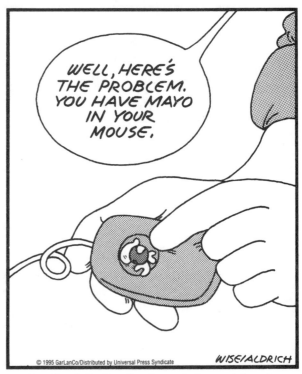

Productivity tip: Don't work through lunch.

Real Life Adventures

Tech support for the techless.

Real Life Adventures

Birds aren't the only ones who peck for food.

When you don't have to get up as early as your mate, it's best not to call attention to it.

Where the Boys Are.

A telltale sign that you're spending
too much time at work.

You don't need a disposable camera
to take disposable pictures.

Real Life Adventures

The Memo Composter.

Real Life Adventures

Just as likely.

Real Life Adventures

Breakfast cereal for men.

Real Life Adventures

How old were you when you realized that sparklers aren't where it's at?

Real Life Adventures

Experience is the best teacher.
And you are not doing well in her class.

Real Life Adventures

Sometimes you don't really have to ask.

Real Life Adventures

Examining your fellow elevator passengers and estimating how close you are to the weight limit is probably not a good idea.

Real Life Adventures

Most people are not at their best first thing in the morning.

Real Life Adventures

The Window of Opportunity is located right next to the Trap Door of Disaster.

Real Life Adventures

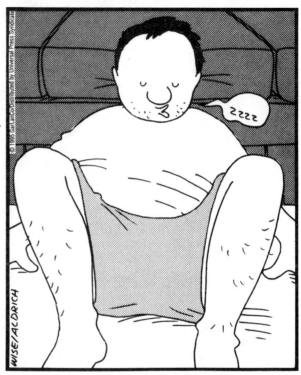

Floor model. As is. Make offer.

Real Life Adventures

Garage sale logic.

Real Life Adventures

Interview With the Umpire.

Real Life Adventures

Real life post-graduate education.

Real Life Adventures

Fake nails for men: to give you that manly, ragged, broken, chewed look in seconds.

Real Life Adventures

When they say "quantities are limited" on home shopping shows, "limited" is a relative term.

Real Life Adventures

At the Comedy Figure Skating Championships.

Real Life Adventures

Why it's called fly-fishing.

Real Life Adventures

Casual day at work gone mad.

Real Life Adventures

**Fiscally, everybody pretty much works
on a system of checks and balances:
lots of checks and no balance.**

Real Life Adventures

If Fred and Ginger danced through your garden.

Real Life Adventures

The point of no return.

Real Life Adventures

Dinner theater.

Real Life Adventures

Taking your kid to work isn't
always such a good idea.

Real Life Adventures

Groomal shower.

Real Life Adventures

There are some things a new parent would do anything to get.

Real Life Adventures

Guy redecorating.

Real Life Adventures

Time travel is going to be a lot
like any other kind of travel.

Real Life Adventures

Business gangs.

Real Life Adventures

A potato being planted.

Real Life Adventures

HERE. SIGN THIS. YOUR MEETING IS AT ELEVEN. YOU'RE GOING TO THE BRIEFING AT TWO. BE BACK HERE BY THREE FOR THE CONFERENCE CALL. STRAIGHTEN YOUR TIE; IT'S CROOKED.

WISE/ALDRICH

Bosses tell people what to do.
Secretaries tell bosses what to do.

Real Life Adventures

At the sweaty T-shirt contest.

Real Life Adventures

Tracking your investment portfolio is part of any good financial strategy.

Real Life Adventures

The Restaurant of Lost Purses.

Real Life Adventures

Why should those little candy hearts be confined to Valentine's Day, when they could be made to sum up your sentiments year-round?

Real Life Adventures

They aren't children: they're tiny tape recorders.

Real Life Adventures

The delicacy most often served at
work is the hot potato.

Real Life Adventures

The eternal struggle between good and evil.

Real Life Adventures

**A device created especially for finding
and picking up lost nails.**

Real Life Adventures

If your kitchen were a restaurant, the health department would close you down.

Real Life Adventures

Lunching through work.

Real Life Adventures

Testing positive for stupidity.

Real Life Adventures

Desperate people do desperate things.

Real Life Adventures

Is there life after birth?

Real Life Adventures

First you talk the talk, then you walk the walk.

Real Life Adventures

Why most of us could never be doctors.

Real Life Adventures

To men, they're *all* mysterious kitchen gadgets.

Real Life Adventures

At least sarcasm is always easy to find.

Real Life Adventures

Polterguests.

Real Life Adventures

**Autumn in the subdivision:
When the leaves fall from the tree.**

Real Life Adventures

Why contractors never return calls.

Real Life Adventures

Party prepoopers.

Real Life Adventures

Many questions are actually statements.

Real Life Adventures

Who says guys are uncomfortable with
public displays of affection?

Real Life Adventures

Picking out a movie seat is only slightly
less complicated than making a movie.

Real Life Adventures

Novels for the do-it-yourselfer.

Real Life Adventures

Shortly after the Scots invented golf,
they invented scotch.

Real Life Adventures

Driving under the influence of the person in the passenger seat.

Real Life Adventures

The more boring the meeting, the faster your butt goes to sleep.

Real Life Adventures

**To cement your relationship,
spend some quality halftime together.**

Real Life Adventures

**4X4s are perfect for the rough terrain their
owners encounter every day.**

Painting the town a really, really light red.

Why it's hard to keep your marriage one long, heavenly, romantic dream.

Real Life Adventures

You have to train them in simple, easy steps, followed by plenty of praise.

Real Life Adventures

There is a definite, scientifically proven link between pantyhose and violence.

Real Life Adventures

Wine tasting.   Beer tasting.

Real Life Adventures

You don't have to go to the movies to experience surround-sound.

Real Life Adventures

WISE/ALDRICH

A small craft warning has just been issued.

Real Life Adventures

WISE/ALDRICH

Why procrastinate now when you can put it off until later?

Real Life Adventures

**Admit it. Your appliances are
smarter than you are.**

Real Life Adventures

**Exercises you can do right at your workstation:
shirking responsibility.**

Real Life Adventures

Why there aren't more operas written
about contemporary life.

Real Life Adventures

Two things no one can understand or explain.

Real Life Adventures

Eggs over easy, my butt.

Real Life Adventures

Shortly after the first tool was invented,
the first tool was borrowed.

Real Life Adventures

Hypnotic trance: a sleeplike state in which the subject is very often at work.

Real Life Adventures

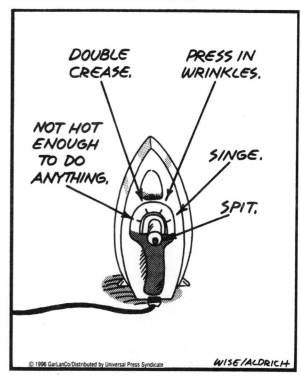

Real-life iron settings.

Real Life Adventures

What the newspeople talk about after the newscast is over but before the camera is off.

Real Life Adventures

Comets aren't the only things that leave trails.

Real Life Adventures

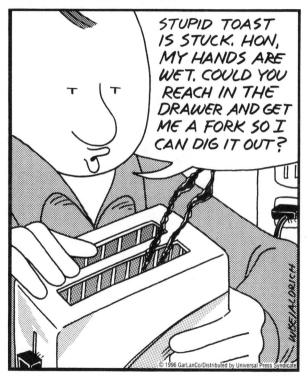

More proof that you shouldn't do your own wiring.

Real Life Adventures

Men, like computers, are often menu-driven.

Real Life Adventures

Truthful menus would be great weight-loss tools.

Real Life Adventures

Why most of us wouldn't make good astronauts.

Real Life Adventures

The new-mommy fashion show.

Real Life Adventures

It's a lot easier to dig ice cream out of the carton if you let it soften a little.

Real Life Adventures

Real Life Adventures

The budget battle goes on in the House.

Real Life Adventures

The buck starts here.

Real Life Adventures

If you're convinced that drinking coffee
sharpens your senses, think again.

Real Life Adventures

You don't have to admit you're wrong.
Someone else is always happy to do it for you.

Real Life Adventures

Sadly, some of us have been
mathematically eliminated.

Real Life Adventures

The only time you know you have a
conscience is when it's guilty.

Real Life Adventures

Born to be a lawyer.

Real Life Adventures

Home theater.

Real Life Adventures

Occasionally we all come up with a criminally bad idea.

It's tough to gather your thoughts when
you have no idea where they are.

Real Life Adventures

A good breakfast gets your whole day off to a good start.

Real Life Adventures

A question for which there is no right answer.

The four C's of diamond buying.

At the Fantasy Camp for Lawyers.

Real Life Adventures

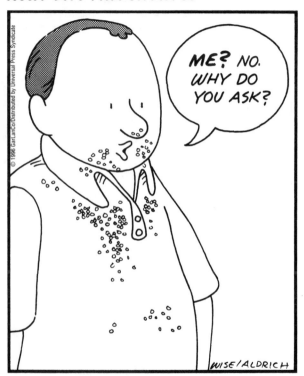

It's hard to sneak a powdered doughnut.

Real Life Adventures

It's not just the guys that pick up the trash who are trash collectors.

Real Life Adventures

Technical terms. **Laymen's terms.**

Real Life Adventures

**Imitation is sometimes the sincerest
form of unemployment.**

Real Life Adventures

The computer generation.

Real Life Adventures

Most accidents happen within twenty-five yards of a car wash.

Real Life Adventures

Plane: used for taking large pieces
of wood off things you meant to
take small pieces off.

Real Life Adventures

Last of the lukewarm lovers.

Real Life Adventures

Don't think of it as shoving stuff under the sofa. Think of it as maximizing your home's storage space.

Real Life Adventures

Some days, life is just a living heck.

Real Life Adventures

Sometimes it's easy to make
your dreams come true.

Real Life Adventures

Lost and found.

Real Life Adventures

Why not sharpen those water-hazard
ball-retrieval skills at home?

Real Life Adventures

"Showing a little leg" is *so* much sexier
for women than for men.

Real Life Adventures

The slightly-longer-than-the-wood-is-thick-screw.

Real Life Adventures

The ruse is over as soon as you shuffle the cards.

Real Life Adventures

http://www.icanbarelyuseacomputer
letalonetheinternet.com

Real Life Adventures

The alternative for those who find having a
"wine cellar" a bit presumptuous.

Real Life Adventures

No pain, no gain.

Real Life Adventures

It's always nice to be recognized by your co-workers for your accomplishments.

Real Life Adventures

Good hygiene and good grooming are not the same thing.

Real Life Adventures

1. Cut out. 2. Hang near work station.

Real Life Adventures

This episode of "Dirty Laundry" was performed before a live audience.

Real Life Adventures

There are those who would contend that the tax code is *in* code.

Real Life Adventures

In power locks, as with brains, the left side doesn't always know what the right side is doing.

Real Life Adventures

Executive summary.